ROCK
& POP

e 3

TRINITY
COLLEGE LONDON

THE EXAM AT A GLANCE

For your Rock & Pop exam you will need to perform a set of **three songs** and one of the **Session skills** assessments, either **Playback** or **Improvising**. You can choose the order in which you play your set-list.

Song 1

Choose a song from this book

OR from www.trinityrock.com

Song 2

Choose a different song from this book

OR from www.trinityrock.com

OR perform a song you have chosen yourself: this could be your own cover version or a song you have written. It should be at the same level as the songs in this book. See the website for detailed requirements.

Song 3: Technical focus

Choose one of the Technical focus songs from this book, which cover three specific technical elements.

Session skills

Choose either **Playback** or **Improvising**.

When you are preparing for your exam please check on **www.trinityrock.com** for the most up-to-date information and requirements as these can change from time to time.

CONTENTS

Tuning track: E, A, D, G with a pause between each note.

Trinity College London's Rock & Pop syllabus and supporting publications have been devised and produced in association with Faber Music and Peters Edition London.

Trinity College London
Registered office:
89 Albert Embankment
London SE1 7TP UK
T + 44 (0)20 7820 6100
F + 44 (0)20 7820 6161
E music@trinitycollege.co.uk
www.trinitycollege.co.uk

Registered in the UK. Company no. 02683033
Charity no. 1014792
Patron HRH The Duke of Kent KG

Copyright © 2012 Trinity College London
First published in 2012 by Trinity College London

Second impression, May 2012

Cover and book design by Chloë Alexander
Brand development by Andy Ashburner @ Caffeinehit (www.caffeinehit.com)
Photographs courtesy of Rex Features Limited.
Printed in England by Caligraving Ltd

Audio produced, mixed and mastered by Tom Fleming
Bass arranged by Tom Fleming
Backing tracks arranged by Tom Fleming
Musicians
Vocals: Bo Walton, Brendan Reilly & Alison Symons
Keyboards: Oliver Weeks
Guitar: Tom Fleming
Bass: Ben Hillyard
Drums: George Double
Studio Engineer: Joel Davies www.thelimehouse.com

ISBN: 978-0-85736-230-8

SONGS SOUND AND VISION

David Bowie
Words and Music by David Bowie

♩ = 106 **Art Rock**   *2 bars count-in*

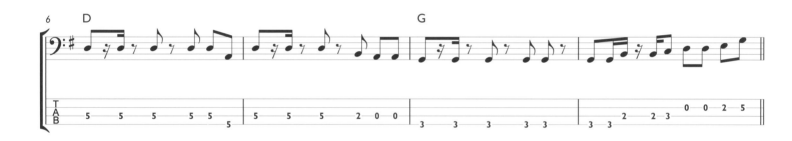

1. Blue, blue, electric blue, that's the colour of my room where I will live.
2. Pale blinds drawn all day, nothing to do, nothing to say.

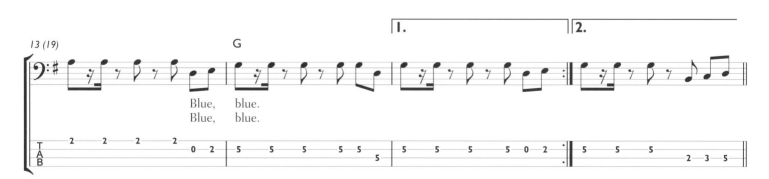

Blue, blue.
Blue, blue.

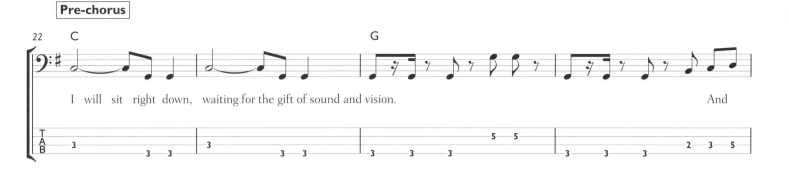

I will sit right down, waiting for the gift of sound and vision. And

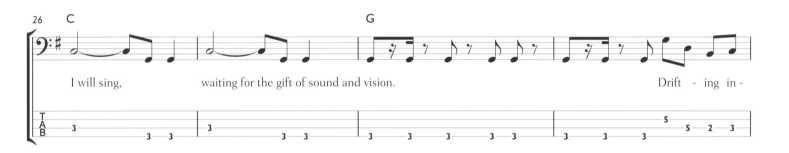

I will sing, waiting for the gift of sound and vision. Drift - ing in-

Chorus

- to my solitude over my head. Don't you wonder some- times

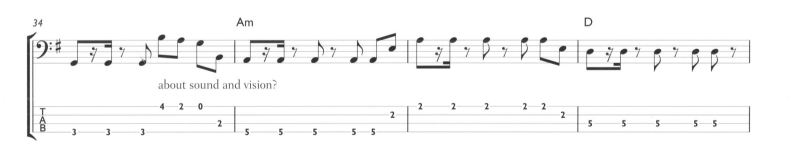

about sound and vision?

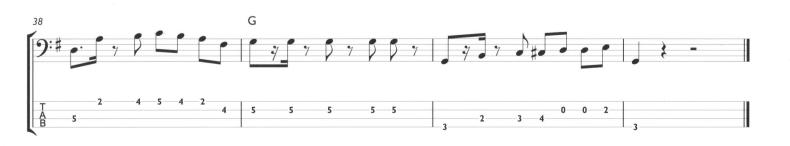

SONGS

SUNSHINE OF YOUR LOVE

TRACK 4 demo / TRACK 5 backing

Cream
Words and Music by Jack Bruce, Peter Brown and Eric Clapton

♩ = 116 **Blues Rock** *2 bars count-in*

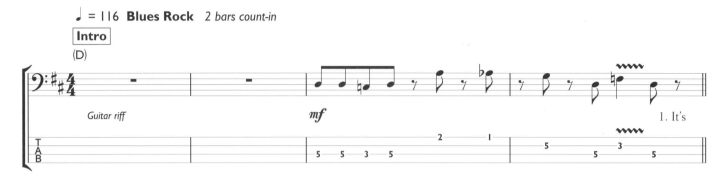

www.trinityrock.com

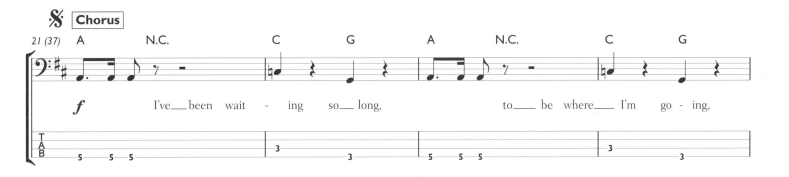

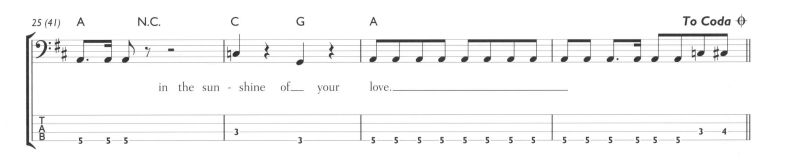

BAND OPTION

SONGS JOHN BARLEYCORN

Traditional
Words and Music Trad.

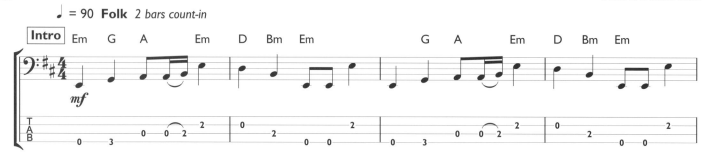

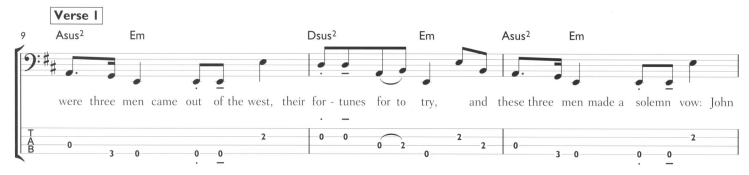

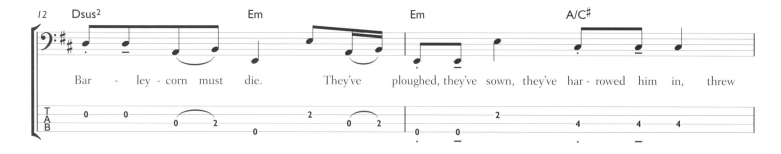

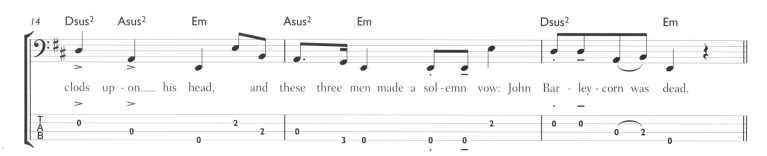

www.trinityrock.com

SONGS ALL DAY AND ALL OF THE NIGHT

The Kinks
Words and Music by Ray Davies

YOUR PAGE

NOTES

MY IRON LUNG

In your exam, you will be assessed on the following technical elements:

1 Dynamic contrast

This is a piece of dynamic contrasts, with the verse and interlude exploding into the raucous chorus and outro. The chorus and outro are both marked *ff* which stands for *fortissimo* – very loud. In contrast, the interlude is marked *p* which stands for *piano* and means quiet. Make sure that these dynamics sound different.

2 Articulation

Articulation is important in 'My Iron Lung'. The ♪ notes in the verse should be played *detaché* (slightly separated), with the exception of the low Fs which are marked with *tenuto* lines. These notes should be played broadly – a bit louder and slightly separated – to give them added importance.

There are several accents (>) in this song. An accent is an emphasis: play the accented notes more strongly than the other notes, so that they ring out. Make the most of the accents, particularly in bars 20 and 36.

3 Playing ♪ evenly

For most of the first page of this song the bass plays repeated ♩♪♪♪♩♪♪♪. Make sure that these notes are played evenly and strictly in time: it is tempting to rush. Practise slowly at first and then gradually build up the speed as your playing becomes secure.

TECHNICAL FOCUS SONGS

MY IRON LUNG

Radiohead

Words and Music by Thomas Yorke, Jonathan Greenwood, Colin Greenwood, Edward O'Brien and Philip Selway

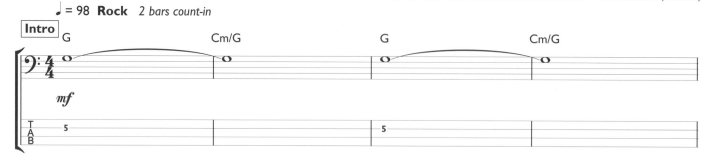

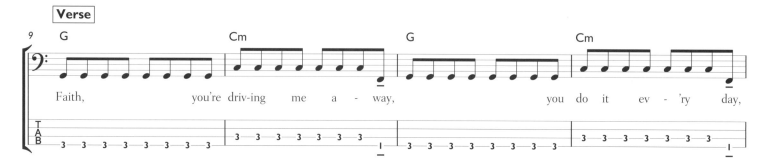

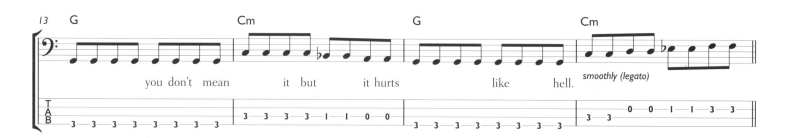

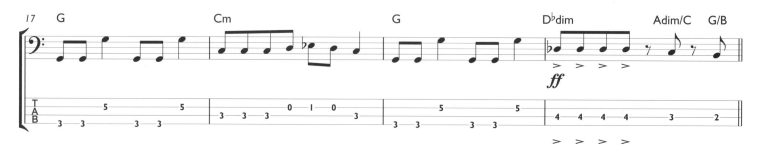

www.trinityrock.com

Faster (♩ = c.108)

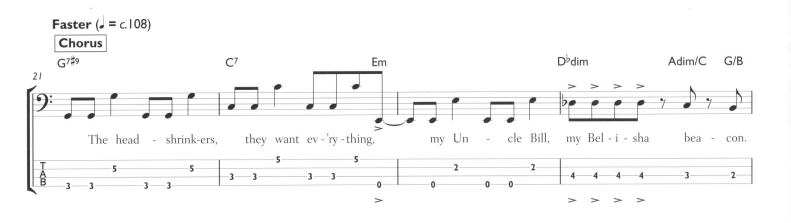

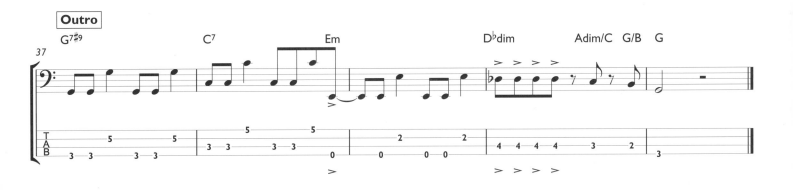

YOUR PAGE NOTES

ADDICTED TO LOVE

In your exam, you will be assessed on the following technical elements:

1 Rhythmic precision

For most of 'Addicted To Love', the bass does not play on the first beat of the bar, but comes in on the second ♪ of each bar. Practise your first entry slowly at first, counting the eight ♪ beats in a bar, so that you can come in exactly on the second ♪:

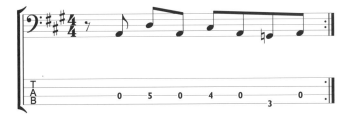

Practise this several times. When you feel confident with the rhythm, gradually build up the speed.

2 Syncopation

Syncopation is where off-beat notes are emphasised. Pay particular attention to the syncopated rhythm in bars 24–26 and bars 28–30. These two rhythms are very similar but differ in the second half of the last bar.

Practise these rhythms until they feel and sound natural: slowly at first, counting eight ♪ beats in a bar and placing your notes carefully. Build up the speed as you become more confident.

3 Articulation

The *staccato* notes in bars 27 and 28 add a slightly funky feel to this passage – you can damp the string with either hand to clip the notes short.

On the CD, the whole band hits accents at bar 31 and 32 together, so make the most of these. The accents on the final two notes are also important: they bring the piece to a definite stop.

ADDICTED TO LOVE

TRACK 12 demo TRACK 13 backing

Robert Palmer
Words and Music by Robert Palmer

♩ = 110 **Rock** *2 bars count-in*

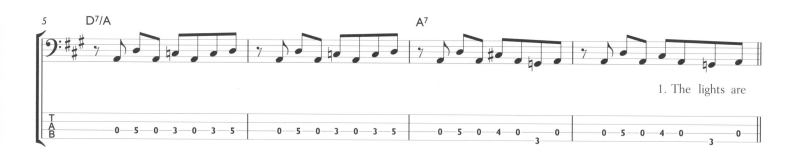

1. The lights are

on,   but you're not home,   your mind   is not your own.   Your heart
(2.) sleep, no,   you can't eat,   there's no doubt,   you're in deep.   Your throat is

sweats,   your body shakes,   a-no-ther kiss   is what it takes.   2. You can't
tight,   you can't breathe,   a-no-ther kiss   is all you

need. Whoa, you like to think that you're im - mune to the stuff, oh yeah.

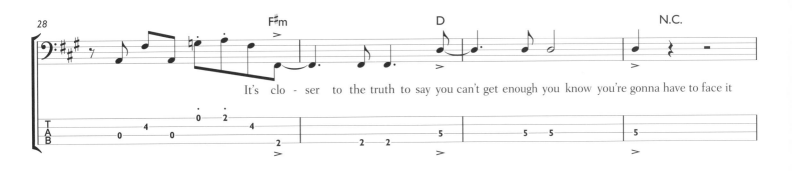

It's clo - ser to the truth to say you can't get enough you know you're gonna have to face it

Outro Chorus

you're addicted to love. Might as well face it you're ad - dic - ted to love. Might

as well face it you're ad - dic - ted to love. Might as well face it you're ad -

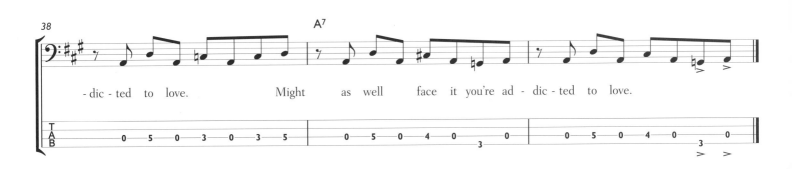

- dic - ted to love. Might as well face it you're ad - dic - ted to love.

ABOUT THE SONGS

SOUND AND VISION

David Bowie

David Bowie was hugely influential during the 1970s. He was effortlessly cool and, with his ever-changing image, achieved cult status. Bowie was one of the first musicians to treat rock concerts as shows with costumes and choreography. During the late 1970s, he lived in Berlin and worked with ex-Roxy Music member Brian Eno. They experimented with electronic music, producing some innovative work.

'Sound And Vision', from David Bowie's electronica-influenced album *Low* (1977), is a synthesiser-based song with funky disco rhythms.

'Sound And Vision' should be played fingerstyle. The syncopated rhythm that underpins the song is really brought to life by the gaps between the notes, so it is important to play the rests as well as the notes. The end of each note is as much a part of the rhythm as the start, so damp each note carefully and rhythmically.

The exceptions to this are at bars 22–23, 26–27 and 32, where the bass plays long notes. Let these ring as long as possible to make a strong contrast with the rest of the piece.

There are some great little fills and variations dotted around the bass part; think about which ones you would like to highlight and play them a little louder than the rest of the song.

'Nothing *to* do, *nothing* to *say*'

SUNSHINE OF YOUR LOVE

Cream

'Sunshine Of Your Love' is one of several classic songs on Cream's highly influential blues-rock album *Disraeli Gears* (1967). The band comprised Eric Clapton (guitar), Jack Bruce (bass) and Ginger Baker (drums) – each of them highly accomplished rock musicians, coming together as probably the first rock supergroup. They started as a blues revival band but their style gradually evolved into hard rock. They were famous for their live performances and long improvised solos.

'Sunshine Of Your Love' opens with one of the most famous riffs ever recorded.

PERFORMANCE · HINTS & TIPS ·

Jack Bruce's famous bass riff lays the foundation for this all-time classic rock song. Apart from the chorus, the bass plays the riff throughout the song, but watch out for variations in the phrasing and articulation. Sometimes the notes are played short to match the guitar; sometimes they are played long and *legato*.

'Sunshine Of Your Love' may be played fingerstyle or with a pick. Left-hand *vibrato* is used in bars 4 and 46 to highlight key notes. In the chorus, damp the ends of notes cleanly to bring out the rests.

This song is also in the guitar and drums books, so you can get together and play it in a band.

'I'll *be* with *you* when *the* stars start *falling*'

JOHN BARLEYCORN

Traffic

'John Barleycorn' is an English folk ballad with a long history dating back to the 16th century. This song – like all songs in the ballad tradition – tells a story. Nobody is really sure who John Barleycorn was, but one idea is that the name represents alcoholic drinks made from barley – a type of corn. There have been many versions of this song, by both folk singers and rock musicians. The 1960s rock band Traffic even named one of their best-selling albums after it – *John Barleycorn Must Die*.

'John Barleycorn' should be played like a folk dance – play it fingerstyle and keep it light.

Make sure that you follow all the articulation markings. Some of the notes in the intro are marked with slurs (⌒). Play the slurred notes as smoothly as you can. The other notes should be more separated. Notes marked *staccato* should be played short and light.

The ♩♪ (in, for example, bar 5) should be played using right-hand palm muting for the first note, which should be released for the second.

This song is also in the vocals, keyboards, guitar and drums books, so you can get together and play it in a band.

'These *three* men *made* a *solemn* vow'

ALL DAY AND ALL OF THE NIGHT

The Kinks

The Kinks were one of the most influential bands of the 1960s. A four-piece London Mod band, they produced short punchy songs, often with high quality lyrics written by their singer Ray Davies. Like many British bands of that time, they began as an R&B group but their style changed over their long career.

The Kinks had a string of hit singles during the 1960s, including 'All Day And All Of The Night' which is built upon a simple sliding power chord riff.

PERFORMANCE · HINTS & TIPS ·

This song can be played fingerstyle or with a pick. The playing should be big and bold: the dynamics range from *mf* (*mezzo forte* = moderately loud) to *ff* (*fortissimo* = very loud).

'All Day And All Of The Night' does not start on the first beat of the bar, but on a pick-up note on the last ♪ of the bar. Listen to the two bars count-in and then count through the guitar riff to help you come in on the ♪ pick-up. Listen carefully to the guitar riff: you start by playing exactly the same rhythm.

The bass solo starting at bar 33 introduces some new rhythmic ideas – let your part sing out here. Be ready for the *crescendo* and the slide between the first two notes of bar 35.

This song is also in the vocals, keyboards, guitar and drums books, so you can get together and play it in a band.

'Girl, *I want* to be *with* you, *all of* the *time*'

MY IRON LUNG

Radiohead

'My Iron Lung' appeared on Radiohead's second album, *The Bends* (1995). The band, whose music is sometimes described as intelligent rock, is not afraid to experiment and takes influences not just from rock music, but also from contemporary classical, jazz, electronic and film music.

'My Iron Lung' is said to be in part the band's reaction to the massive success of their 1993 hit 'Creep', comparing it to an iron lung which kept the band going while at the same time holding them back.

'My Iron Lung' should be played fingerstyle. It opens with two long tied **o** notes. Let these ring on for their full value. Both notes last for eight beats: make sure that you hold them on for their full value.

Inject as much energy as you can into the chorus and outro, while keeping your playing clean and controlled.

Bar 16 is marked *legato*. Play this section smoothly, contrasting with the passage of detached notes starting at bar 5.

'The *headshrinkers* they *want* ev'rything'

ADDICTED TO LOVE

Robert Palmer

Robert Palmer had a long career that spanned five decades. Before becoming a solo artist he played in bands, including the Alan Bown Set and Vinegar Joe. He was known for his distinctive, soulful voice and eclectic mix of musical styles, from blues and soul to reggae and jazz.

'Addicted To Love' is taken from the album *Riptide* (1985) and is his most well-known song. It became famous partly because of its iconic video, directed by Terence Donovan, in which Palmer is surrounded by identically-clad, heavily made-up female bass players.

'Addicted To Love' may be played fingerstyle or with a pick. An unusual feature of the song is that the bass almost never plays on the first beat of the bar. Because of this, it is especially important to feel the pulse of the music internally: you need to keep the tempo solid.

Watch out for the accidentals throughout.

'Your *heart* sweats, *your* body *shakes*'

For your exam, you can choose either Playback or Improvising (see page 28).
If you choose Playback, you will be asked to play some music you have not seen
or heard before.

In the exam, you will be given the song chart and the examiner will play a recording
of the music. You will hear several two-bar or four-bar phrases on the recording:
you should play each of them straight back in turn. There's a rhythm track going
throughout, which helps you keep in time. There should not be any gaps in the music.

In the exam you will have two chances to play with the recording:
- First time – for practice
- Second time – for assessment.

You should listen to the audio, copying what you hear; you can also read the music.
Here are some practice song charts which are also on the CD in this book.

Don't forget that the Playback test can include requirements which may not be
shown in these examples, including those from earlier grades. Check the parameters
at www.trinityrock.com to prepare for everything which might come up in your exam.

'I really *like*
the *way*
music *looks* on *paper.*
It *looks* like *art*
to *me*'

Steve Vai

Practice playback 1

Practice playback 2

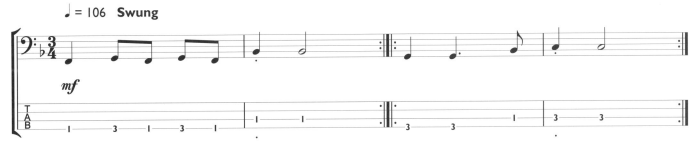

SESSION SKILLS

IMPROVISING

For your exam, you can choose either Playback (see page 26), or Improvising. If you choose to improvise, you will be asked to improvise over a backing track that you haven't heard before in a specified style.

In the exam, you will be given a song chart and the examiner will play a recording of the backing track. The backing track consists of a passage of music played on a loop. You should improvise a bass line which fits the track.

In the exam you will have two chances to play with the recording:
- First time – for practice
- Second time – for assessment.

Here are some improvising charts for practice which are also on the CD in this book.

Don't forget that the Improvising test can include requirements which may not be shown in these examples, including those from earlier grades. Check the parameters at www.trinityrock.com to prepare for everything which might come up in your exam.

Practice improvisation 1

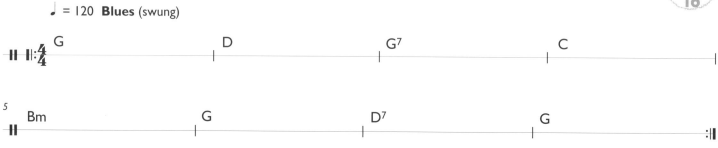

Practice improvisation 2

CHOOSING A SONG FOR YOUR EXAM

There are lots of options to help you choose your three songs for the exam.
For Songs 1 and 2, you can choose a song which is:

- from this book
- from www.trinityrock.com

Or for Song 2 you can choose a song which is:

- sheet music from a printed or online source
- your own arrangement of a song or a song you have written yourself
  (see page 30).

You can play the song unaccompanied or with a backing track (minus the bass part).
If you like, you can create a backing track yourself (or with friends), or you could add
your own vocals – or both.

For Grade 3, the song should last between one-and-a-half and three-and-a-half
minutes, and the level of difficulty should be similar to your other songs. When
choosing a song, think about:

- Does it work on my instrument?
- Are there any technical elements that are too difficult for me? (If so, perhaps
  save it for when you do the next grade.)
- Do I enjoy playing it?
- Does it work with my other pieces to create a good set-list?

See www.trinityrock.com for further information and advice on choosing your
own song.

SHEET MUSIC

You must always bring an original copy of the book or a download sheet with
email certificate for each song you perform in the exam. If you choose to write
your own song you must provide the examiner with a copy of the sheet music.
Your music can be:

- a lead sheet with lyrics, chords and melody line
- a chord chart with lyrics
- a full score using conventional staff notation
- see page 30 for details on presenting a song you have written yourself.

The title of the song and your name should be on the sheet music.

WRITING YOUR OWN SONG

You can play a song that you have written yourself for one of the choices in your exam. For Grade 3, your song should last between one-and-a-half and three-and-a-half minutes. It is sometimes difficult to know where to begin, however. Here are some suggestions for starting points:

- **A rhythm**: A short repeated rhythm will often underpin an entire song. Start by writing a couple of short rhythms here:

- **A riff**: A riff is a short rhythm which is repeated over and over. A short repeated riff will often underpin an entire song. Write a couple of riffs here:

WRITING YOUR SONG DOWN

Rock and pop music is often written as a **lead sheet** with the lyrics (if there are any), chords and a melody line.

- As a bass player, you may want to write your part on a **five-line stave** or as **tab**. Both have been used for the songs in this book.

- You can, if you prefer, use a **graph** or **table** to represent your music, as long as it is clear to anyone else (including the examiner) how the song goes.

- **Instruments**: Which instruments will play your song? You could just use keyboard, bass and drums, or you could add vocals, guitar and any other instruments.

There are plenty of other ways of starting: perhaps with a melody, chord sequence or a lyric, for example.

You will also need to consider the **structure** of your song (verse and chorus, 12-bar blues, and so on) and the **style** it is in (blues, hard rock, etc.).

There are many choices to be made – which is why writing a song is such a rewarding thing to do.

PLAYING IN A BAND

Playing in a band is exciting: it can be a lot of fun and, as with everything, the more you do it, the easier it gets. It is very different from playing on your own. Everyone contributes to the overall sound: the most important skill you need to develop is listening.

For a band to sound good, the players need to be 'together' – that mainly means keeping in time with each other, but also playing at the same volume, and with the same kind of feeling.

Your relationship with the other band members is also important. Talk with them about the music you play, the music you like, and what you'd like the band to achieve short-term and long-term.

Band rehearsals are important – you should not be late, tired or distracted by your mobile phone! Being positive makes a huge difference. Try to create a friendly atmosphere in rehearsals so that everybody feels comfortable trying out new things. Don't worry about making mistakes: that is what rehearsals are for.

'John Barleycorn' on page 8 and 'All Day And All Of The Night' on page 10 are arranged for band. You will find parts for vocals, guitar, keyboard and drums in the other Trinity Rock & Pop Grade 3 books or available online. There are also parts for 'Sunshine Of Your Love' in Trinity Rock & Pop Grade 3 Guitar and Drums books. Trinity offers exams for groups of musicians at various levels. The songs arranged for bands are ideal to include as part of a set-list for these exams. Have a look at the website for more details.

HINTS AND TIPS

- Record your practice sessions and listen carefully to the recordings. Which sections worked well and which had problems? How will you improve the sections with problems?

- In some songs you will play a supporting role; at other times you may take more of a lead. In both cases you need to listen to the overall group as well as to your own part. Be aware of how you affect the sound – every player should make their own distinct contribution to the overall sound.

- Nothing beats the thrill of performing live in front of an audience. Organise a gig for a few friends. It can be a small gig in someone's house – the important thing is to get used to playing in front of other people. Gigs can be nerve-wracking at first, but try to relax and enjoy them.

PLAYING WITH BACKING TRACKS

The CD contains demos and backing tracks of all the songs in the book. The additional songs at www.trinityrock.com also come with demos and backing tracks.

- In your exam, you should perform with the backing track, or you can create your own (see below).
- The backing tracks begin with a click track, which sets the tempo and helps you start accurately.
- Be careful to set the balance between the volume of the backing track and your instrument.
- Listen carefully to the backing track to ensure you are playing in time.

If you are creating your own backing track here are some further tips:
- Make sure the sound quality is of a good standard.
- Think carefully about the instruments/sounds you are putting on the backing track.
- Avoid copying what you are playing on the backing track – it should support not duplicate.
- Do you need to include a click track at the beginning?

COPYRIGHT IN A SONG

If you are a singer or songwriter it is important to know about copyright. When someone writes a song or creates an arrangement they own the copyright (sometimes called 'the rights') to that version. The copyright means that other people cannot copy it, sell it, perform it in a concert, make it available online or record it without the owner's permission or the appropriate licence. When you write a song you automatically own the copyright to it, which means that other people cannot copy your work. But, just as importantly, you cannot copy other people's work, or perform it in public without their permission or the appropriate licence.

Points to remember

- You can create a cover version of a song and play it in an exam or other non-public performance.
- You cannot record your cover version and make your recording available to others (by copying it or uploading it to a website) without the appropriate licence.
- You do own the copyright of your own original song, which means that no one is allowed to copy it.
- You cannot copy someone else's song without their permission or the appropriate licence.